C000126225

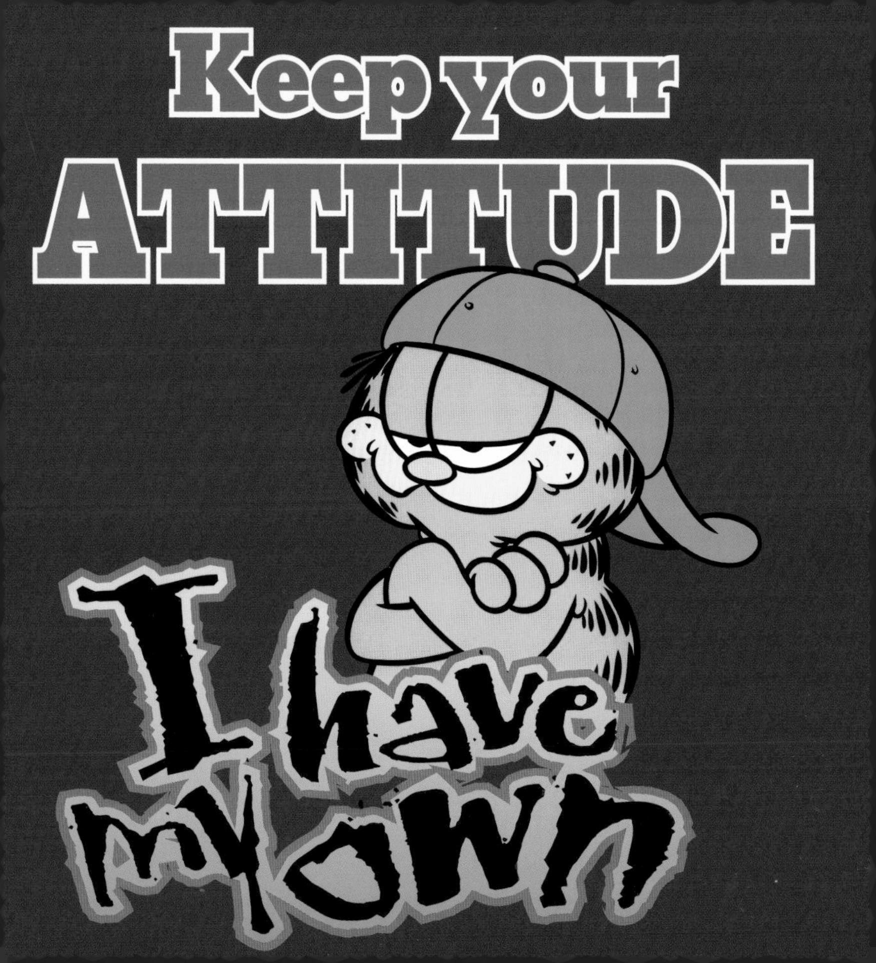
Keep your
ATTITUDE
I have
my own

First published in 2007 by
Ravette Publishing Ltd
Unit 3, Tristar Centre, Star Road,
Partridge Green, West Sussex RH13 8RA

ISBN: 978-1-84161-278-2

Keep your
ATTITUDE

I have my own

ℛ
RAVETTE PUBLISHING

START EACH DAY WITH A SMILE AND GET IT OVER WITH

WHAT'S NOT TO LIKE?

READ MY LIPS

WHAT ABOUT MY NEEDS?

COMPUTE THIS!

I DON'T DO PERKY

TALK TO
THE
PAW

YOU WANNA PIECE OF ME?

TAP
TAP TAP

YOU AND WHAT WHAT ARMY?

Is that your face, or did your pants fall down?

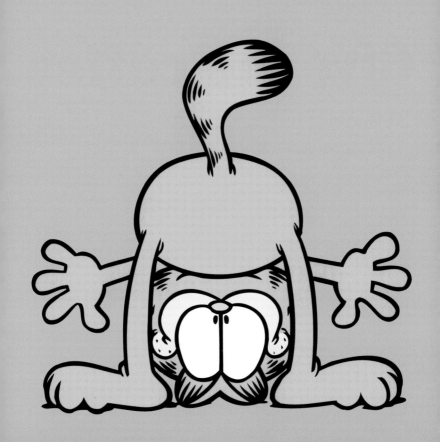

Give me coffee and no one gets hurt

MY WAY OR THE HIGHWAY!

EVERYONE'S ENTITLED TO MY OPINION

I'd love
to help you out ...
which way
did you come in?

DOWNLOAD THIS!

I'M IN A LEAGUE OF MY OWN

WELL,

DUH!

GET A LIFE

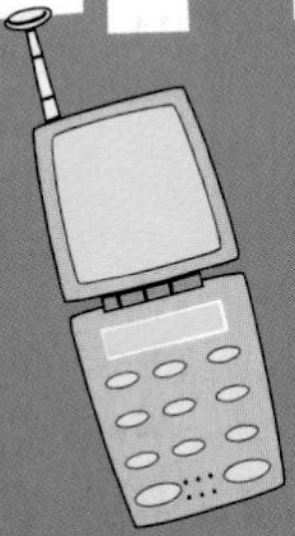

Other GARFIELD Gift Books published by Ravette ...

	ISBN	Price
Gift Books (hardback)		
Don't Know Don't Care	978-1-84161-279-9	£4.99
I Don't Do Ordinary	978-1-84161-281-2	£4.99
Get A Grip	978-1-84161-282-9	£4.99
Little Books (paperback)		
C-c-c-caffeine	978-1-84161-183-9	£2.50
Food 'n' Fitness	978-1-84161-145-7	£2.50
Laughs	978-1-84161-146-4	£2.50
Love 'n' Stuff	978-1-84161-147-1	£2.50
Surf 'n' Sun	978-1-84161-186-0	£2.50
The Office	978-1-84161-184-6	£2.50
Zzzzzz	978-1-84161-185-3	£2.50

All Garfield books are available at your local bookshop or from the publisher at the address below.

Just send your order with your payment and name and address details to:-
Ravette Publishing, Unit 3, Tristar Centre, Star Road, Partridge Green,
West Sussex RH13 8RA (tel: 01403 711443   email: ravettepub@aol.com)

Prices and availability are subject to change without prior notice.

Please enclose a cheque or postal order made payable to Ravette Publishing
to the value of the cover price of the books and allow the following for UK p&p:-

70p for the first book + 40p for each additional book.